THE ADVENTURES
OF PRADA ENCHILADA

The doorbell rang. He jumped off the couch, thinking who stood beyond the door.

It was Mimi Tortellini dressed up and ready for a tour. "Where are we off to now?" asked Prada. "To travel the world," replied Mimi. "Great! There is much to see in the world," uttered Prada, "Australia, Europe, Antarctica, South and North America, Africa and Asia; seven continents in all, which spin on a globe shaped like a ball."

Mimi then grabbed Prada's hand and headed out the door, ready to explore.

Prada and Mimi hopped on a plane, knowing they could not take a train.

The plane flew up high taking them into the sky. They passed over oceans and clouds until they reached the smallest continent of the bunch, Australia.

Then along came a breeze, which forced the plane to land among a forest of eucalyptus trees.

Prada got out the plane to make sure everything was all right, while Mimi wandered about taking in the sights.

Prada then heard a loud roar, not knowing what was in store. He ran over to Mimi, "Is everything okay?" asked Prada.

"Yes! I am just in awe of the koala holding onto the tree with its bare claws," said Mimi. "While it is snoring; did you know that koalas can be pretty boring?" asked Prada. Koalas usually sleep up to 18 hours a day, which leaves no time for play.

Off they went back into
the sky, to see another
continent nearby.

The plane landed in Europe; the second smallest continent of seven. To their surprise reindeer ran toward them in a herd of eleven.

"Are those reindeer?" asked Mimi. "Why, yes!" replied Prada, "Did you know that their antlers fall off different times of the year?" "Oh, dear!" shouted Mimi. The old males' fall off in early winter, the females' fall off in the summer and the young males' fall off in the spring. Can you spot the females whose antlers are missing?

4, Incredible! After enjoying the scene, it was time to hop back into their machine.

They flew south floating over the ocean, when Mimi suddenly noticed some motion. "I think there is something moving in the water," said Mimi. The plane drifted slowly overhead, while Prada looked at the map and said, "We are in Antarctica, which is the third smallest continent out of seven."

That is when a blue whale peeked out its head. "Look, I knew there was something moving about," said Mimi. "Ah! A blue whale; I wonder if it is sleeping," said Prada. "Sleeping? I did not know whales slept," replied Mimi.

Prada stated, "Why yes, whales sleep too Mimi. They shut down half of their brain while they sleep. This allows them to come up for air without drowning." Now can you help us count the number of blue whales within our surroundings.

2, *Terrific!* The plane crossed the seas impossibly fast until they reached the Americas at last.

"Back in America," said Mimi. "South America to be exact," responded Prada. South America is the fourth continent that falls in the middle of seven. They stepped off the plane, into a watery domain.

"Yuck, we have landed in a swamp," said Mimi. To Prada's surprise, anacondas were roaming freely.

"I did not know that snakes could live in water,"
uttered Mimi. "An anaconda's eyes and nose lay
on top of their head, which allows it to breathe in
water," said Prada. "Ooh-eh how many can you
see?" said Mimi.

Prada and Mimi jumped back on the plane to go see the next continent, and all its terrain.

They reached North America, which is the third largest continent of seven. From the plane they noticed a bison grazing. "Did you know that bison have poor eyesight, but their sense of smell is amazing," said Prada.

"Look over there, some more stand observing with their brown hair," said Mimi. Can you count the number of bison that are grazing and observing?

8, Correct! After they finished the task, it was off to explore Africa at last.

Africa is the second largest continent amongst seven. Mimi looked out the plane to notice some lions full of manes.

"I wonder why some of the lions have manes, while the other ones seem rather plain?" expressed Mimi.

Prada explained, "Male lions grow manes, but the females do not." The plane slowly landed. Now let's see how many male lions we can spot.

3, Super! As Prada boarded the flight, he wondered what else they might sight.

Then they were off; to see a continent that was not small at all. Asia is the largest continent of the bunch. Which I am sure you had a hunch.

The plane landed in a dense jungle. Mimi stepped out and took a little stumble. That is when Prada spotted some eyes peeking out from the grass. Mimi shouted, "Oh no! What is it?"

All of a sudden, an orange, white, and black tail went past. "Ah, it's a tiger," said Prada, "Did you know that tigers use their stripes to camouflage from their prey?" Now can you spot how many tigers are hiding during the day?

Now it was time for the plane
to start soaring.

They made it back safely to North America. Mimi hopped out the plane to inspect the area. "What is it?" asked Prada.

Color, cut and match the animal to the right continent.

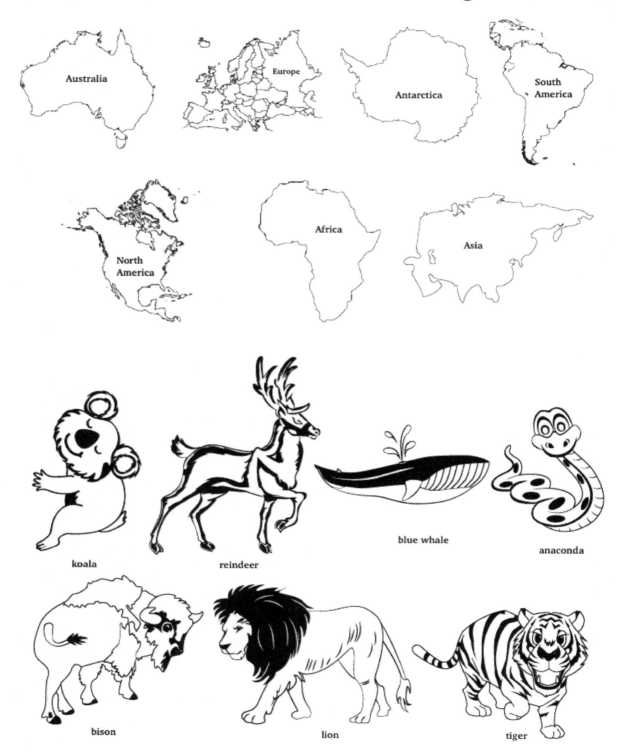

Make your own Pradagram (Hologram)

STEP 1

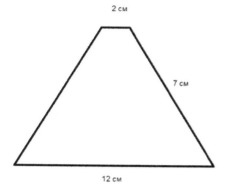

2 см
7 см
12 см

SUPPLIES

- Plastic CD Cover or Acetate Sheet

- Scissors or X-acto Knife

- Tape or Glue

STEP 2

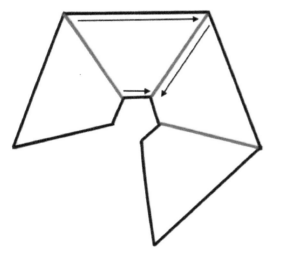

DIRECTIONS

1. Measure out all 4 sides to make a pyramid.

2. Duplicate the exact pyramid 4 times.

3. Cut out pyramids.

4. Glue/Tape all 4 sides together.

Scan QR Code to download PradaGram app

STEP 3

Place pyramid on top of downloaded app
via phone/tablet. Then press play on screen.

CPSIA information can be obtained
at www.ICGtesting.com
Printed in the USA
BVOW05s2319050617

486070BV00003B/3/P